Ladybird Reade

ROALD DAHL

The Giraffe, the Pelly and Me
Activity Book

Based on the original title by Roald Dahl
Illustrated by Quentin Blake

Written by Hazel Geatches
Song lyrics on page 16 written by Wardour Studios

 Singing *    Reading   Speaking   **?** Critical thinking

abc Spelling   Writing   Listening *

*To complete these activities, listen to tracks 2, 3, and 4 of the Reader audio download available at www.ladybirdeducation.co.uk

1 Look and read.
Write the correct words on the lines.

| man | giraffe | monkey | boy | police | pelican |

1 a ____man____

2 a ____

3 a ____

4 a ____

5 the ____

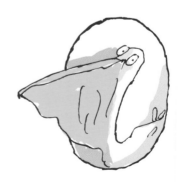

6 a ____

2 Look and read.
Write the phrases in the correct boxes.

| is short | are animals | has a big beak |

| can fly | can't fly | can clean windows |

| has a long neck | are friends | is tall |

the Giraffe	the Giraffe and the Pelican	the Pelican
	can clean windows	

3

3 **Look, match, and write the words.**

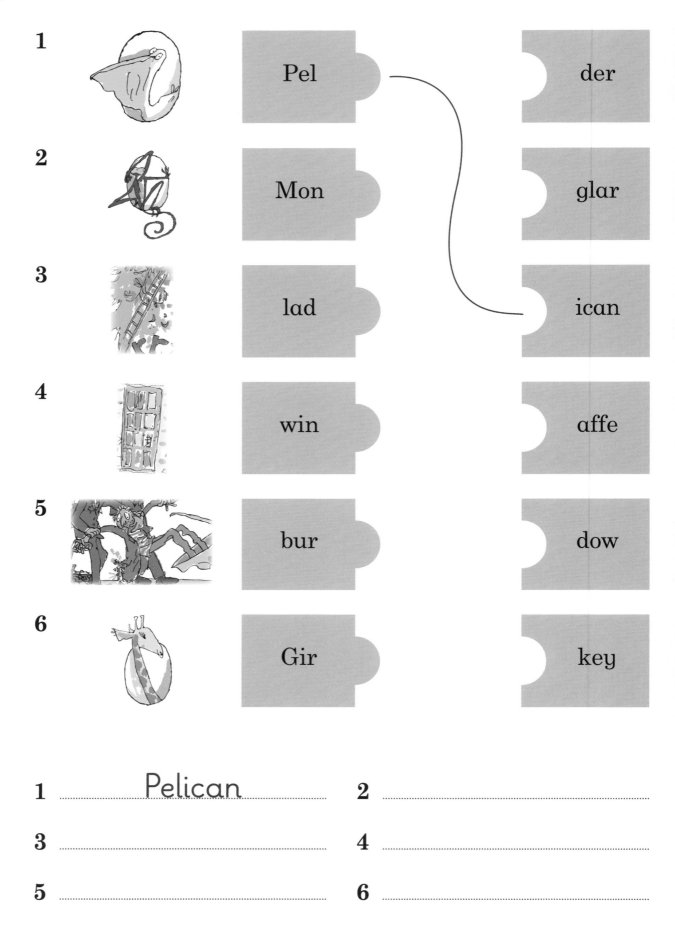

1   Pel   der

2   Mon   glar

3   lad   ican

4   win   affe

5   bur   dow

6   Gir   key

1   Pelican   2

3   4

5   6

4

4 **Read, and circle the correct words.**

1

There was an (old)/ **new** house near the boy's home.

2

One day, the house had a new, **short** / **tall** door.

3

In one window, there was a **big** / **small** pelican.

4

The Duke had lots of **dirty** / **clean** windows.

5 Listen, color, draw, and write.
Use the colors below. 🎧*

6 **Read the text. Choose the correct words and write them next to 1—6.** 📖 ✏️

threw   came   opened   flew   jumped   went

The Pelican [1] ___threw___ the water out of his

beak and [2] _____ up to the window.

He [3] _____ into the room. When he flew down

again, a loud noise [4] _____ from his beak.

When the police came, the Pelican [5] _____

his beak, and the police [6] _____ on the burglar.

7 **Circle the correct pictures.**

1 Who cleans the
windows?

2 Who holds the water? ⓐ  ⓑ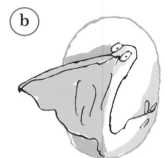

3 Who is the ladder? ⓐ  ⓑ

4 Who helps the
animals?

ⓐ  ⓑ

5 Who has very
dirty windows?

ⓐ  ⓑ

8

8 Work with a friend.
Ask and answer questions about the picture.

1 How many animals are there?

There are three animals.

2 How many people are there?

3 Which animal is the tallest?

4 Which person is older?

9 **Do the crossword.**

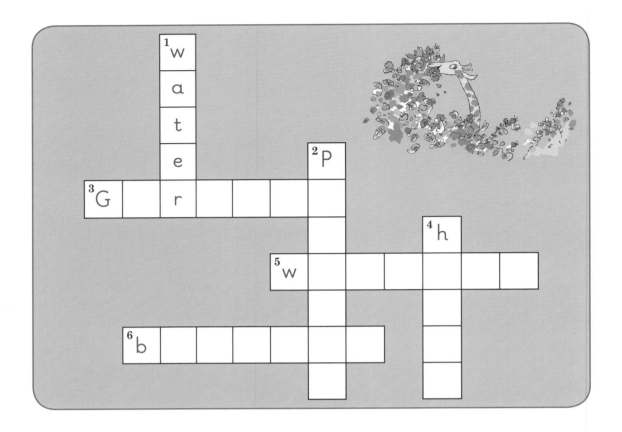

¹w
a
t
e
³G r
²P
⁴h
⁵w
⁶b

Down

1 When the animals clean windows, the Pelly holds this.

2 He has a very big beak.

4 In the past, this was a candy store.

Across

3 She has a very long neck.

5 The animals clean these when they are dirty.

6 He took things from the Duke's cupboard.

1 "We never stop to drink tea."   ....C......

2 "We can clean windows!"   ....

3 "With friends like us—"   ....

4 "Who needs a ladder?"   ....

5 "We work really hard."   ....

6 "The Giraffe, the Pelly and Me!"   ....

11 **Draw a picture of Billy. Read the questions and write about Billy.** 📖 ✏️ ❓

1 What's your name?

My name is Billy.

2 Where do you live?

3 What do you want to do?

4 Who are your friends?

12 Who said this?

Billy

the Giraffe

the Pelican

the Monkey

the Duke

1 "Jump in."   the Pelican

2 "We can clean windows!"

3 "My wife's jewels!
Call the police!"

4 "I would like to open a
candy store there."

5 "Nothing is too high for me!"

13 Look, and write the missing letters.

| fri Pel hou Mon pol ani bea lad bur jew win Gir |

1 f r i e n d s

2 .... i c a n

3 .... e l s

4 .... d e r

5 .... k e y

6 .... d o w

7 .... m a l s

8 .... a f f e

9 .... i c e

10 .... s e

11 .... g l a r

12 .... k

14 Work with a friend. Help the police catch the burglar. Use the words in the box.

turn right   go straight   turn left   go to the end

Turn right. Then, turn left . . .

The Giraffe, the Pelly and Me,
We can clean windows, you see!
Giraffe's neck goes high,
She'll get as high as the sky,
And the windows are clean as can be.

The man in the car said, "Come and help me,
The Duke needs his windows
Cleaned, you see."
The Duke's house was so tall,
No one could reach up at all,
But Giraffe's long neck made it easy.

Giraffe said, "Someone is taking your things!"
The Duke called the police,
Then heard Pelican's wings.
He came down on his feet
With a man in his beak,
The burglar was caught with the things.

The Giraffe, the Pelly and Me,
We can clean windows, you see!
Giraffe's neck goes high,
She'll get as high as the sky,
And the windows are clean as can be.

*To complete this activity, listen to track 4 of the Reader audio download available at **www.ladybirdeducation.co.uk**